One, Two, Three for Fun

Story by Muriel Stanek

Pictures by Seymour Fleishman

Albert Whitman & Company • Chicago

TEXT © 1967 BY MURIEL STANEK; ILLUSTRATIONS © 1967 BY SEYMOUR FLEISHMAN
LIBRARY OF CONGRESS CATALOG CARD 67-26519
PUBLISHED SIMULTANEOUSLY IN CANADA BY GEORGE J. MCLEOD, LTD., TORONTO
LITHOGRAPHED IN THE UNITED STATES OF AMERICA

A Note About This Book. . .

Children's play offers a happy background for building number concepts. Little children quickly learn to count by rote, but true and deeper understandings of number concepts require concrete experiences. In this book, girls and boys see numerical values grow out of everyday play activities. The settings are familiar—city streets, backyards, playgrounds, classrooms, and parks. Using numbers thus becomes a natural part of everyday living.

Children soon learn to recognize simple quantities at a glance, without counting the individual figures in a group. This ability is useful when simple number operations are taught. As the introduction of numbers progresses in the pages that follow, the simplest addition facts are informally introduced. When two friends are playing, for example, and another child joins them, it is easy to think, "Two and one are three."

An observant girl or boy will notice that the leaves on the plant beside each decorative number correspond to the number. This device also makes the meaning of "many" clear.

Position is introduced as children are shown waiting for a turn. The meaning of "first" and "last" is easily developed. These scenes, incidentally, help establish such courteous behavior as waiting in line and taking turns.

Whether children in a group enjoy ONE, TWO, THREE FOR FUN or a single child chooses the book to examine alone, there's both pleasure and learning in store.

—MURIEL STANEK

One, two, three—
look at me!
I can skate all by myself.
Skating's fun for just one.

one

A puzzle is fun
for just one

and so is reading a book.

17070

Sometimes it's fun to be alone.
When I'm the only one, I color—
then all the crayons are mine.

Blowing bubbles—
that's fun for just one.

See bubbles floating
all around,
then
POP
they're gone!

I like to be the only one
who's swinging.
Higher and higher I go
without the help of anyone.

I have a little bed
just big enough for one.
It's nice to snuggle
under the covers
all by myself.
Just me!

2
two

One and one
are two.
A secret's fun
for two
to share.
Buzz.
Buzz.
Buzz.

Two friends talk on the telephone.
"Hello, how are you?"
"Hello, I'm fine. Thank you."

Bunk beds are made
for two.

I'm on top,

you're down below.

When we are two
a seesaw is fun.

You go up
and I come down.

Climbing a fence is easy for two.
You help me and I'll help you.

three

Two and one are three.
One, two, three
for jumping rope—
two to turn the rope
and one to jump.

Three of us play hide and seek.
I'll shut my eyes
and you two hide.
"Ready or not
—here I come!"

There are three of us.
What can we play?
"London Bridge Is Falling Down!"

Three and one are four.
Four friends are just right
for a square table.
"Please have a cookie?"
"Yes, thank you."

four

Tug-of-war is fun for four.
Two on your side, two on mine.

How many on our merry-go-round?
Four of us—
three boys and a girl.
Hold on, hold on!

5 five

Four and one make five.
Let's make a tent.
Four of us have the blanket.
Who's in the middle
holding up the pole?

One, two, three, four, five!
Clear the way for our parade.
March, march, here we come!

Five to play a circle game—
What will it be?
"Ring-Around-a-Rosy!"

Five to make a rhythm band—
What can we play?
"Twinkle, Twinkle, Little Star!"

many

More than one, more than two.
More than three or four or five.
What do we say? That's many!
Many of us stand in line,
waiting for a treat.

Many of us in a line
waiting for a drink.
I'm last!
But soon. . .

I'm first again!

One, two,
three:
We have
fun!